# Bubble
# Attack

**Writt**

**Illustrate**

## Titles in Full Flight 5

---

Badger Publishing Limited
15 Wedgwood Gate, Pin Green Industrial Estate,
Stevenage, Hertfordshire SG1 4SU
Telephone: 01438 356907. Fax: 01438 747015
www.badger-publishing.co.uk
enquiries@badger-publishing.co.uk

Bubble Attack   ISBN 978 1 84691 124 8

Series Editor: Jonny Zucker
Publisher: David Jamieson
Commissioning Editor: Carrie Lewis
Editor: Paul Martin
Design: Fiona Grant
Illustration: Seb Camagajevac (Beehive Illustration)

# Bubble Attack

## Contents

# 1. In the beginning...

Paul South was small for his age. That made him easy to bully. One day, Paul was on his way home when he heard a voice behind him.

Suddenly a huge bubble appeared from nowhere. Without knowing why, Paul stepped inside the bubble.

Paul had not seen the bubbles on TV.

Paul held on. The bubble began to move.

The bubble began to follow the road.

Paul did not know it, but the bubble was not joking. It was using him to find out where London was!

So Paul got inside the new bubble.
Soon they had got to London.

Suddenly Paul had a very bad feeling about the bubble.

# 3. Bubble trouble

The river police were not very happy.

The bubble pushed the police boat into the water.

The bubble rolled over to the Houses of Parliament.

Hey, you there. Stop in the name of the law!

Bubble, I don't like this at all. I want to get out.

You can't get out, Paul. It is not safe!

# 4. Get the army!

Before very long, the army turned up.

The bubbles picked up the tanks and
took them over to the river.

Then they let the tanks fall into the water.

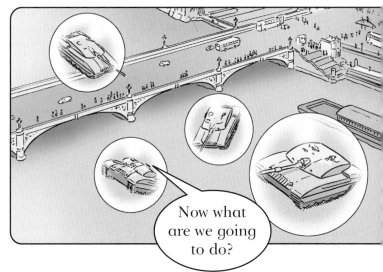

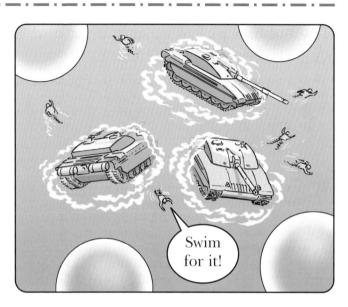

The police had tried to stop the bubbles. The army had tried too. Now it was time for the air force.

# 5. Apple time?

I've got a feeling that this might just work.

TV crews had come to find out what was going on with the bubbles. Nobody knew what to do to stop them.

A short time later, Paul was back in the sky…

Down there. You have to drop it on the bubbles. It's our only hope!

This is just silly. They have tried to shoot guns at the bubbles. They have tried to shoot them with tanks and rockets. Now what are they going to do? Drop water on them?

As soon as the strange-coloured rain
hit the bubbles, they began to pop.
Soon all the bubbles were falling apart.

As soon as the bubbles had gone, the plane came in to land.

It's apple juice! They were dropping apple juice from that plane.

# 6. Here we go again

After that, life went back to the way it always had been for Paul South. Well, almost…